DREAM TO WIN

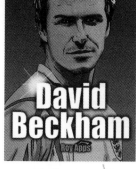

David Beckham

Roy Apps

978 0 7496 8232 3

Other titles in the series:

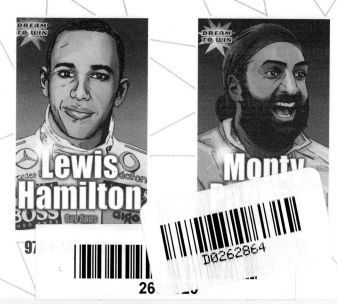

Lewis Hamilton

Monty

97

26

For my niece Katie Layson

First published in 2008 by
Franklin Watts
338 Euston Road
London NW1 3BH

Franklin Watts Australia
Level 17/207 Kent Street
Sydney NSW 2000

Text © Roy Apps 2008
Illustrations © Chris King 2008
Cover design by Peter Scoulding

A CIP catalogue record for this book
is available from the British Library.

ISBN: 978 0 7496 8235 4

Dewey Classification: 796.358'092

1 3 5 7 9 10 8 6 4 2

Printed in Great Britain

Franklin Watts is a division of Hachette Children's Books,
an Hachette Livre UK company.
www.hachettelivre.co.uk

Hope Powell

Roy Apps

Illustrated by Chris King

FRANKLIN WATTS
LONDON • SYDNEY

Chapter One:
The Best Player on the Street

The boy kicked the football out from underneath the wheel of a parked car. He looked down the street. Two empty cans marked the other side's goalposts. He sprinted towards them, the ball at his feet. Nothing could stop him from scoring now.

He was new to the area and wanted to show that he was the best player around. A small kid from the opposition was charging towards him, so he swerved to the left in a dummy move. Then he ran on.

He'd gone four or five paces before he looked down and saw that the ball was no longer at his feet. He stopped. That little kid must've taken the ball off him without his even knowing it! Who *was* he?

The boy turned round and was just in time to see the little kid thumping the ball past the goalkeeper at the other end of the road. As it crashed into a rusty old dustbin, he watched the opposition team erupt into cheers.

A couple of other players on his side were shaking their heads in disbelief. "Who *is* that kid?" he asked them.

"That's my sister," said one of them, with a sigh.

"Her name's Hope Powell," added his friend. "And she's the best player on the street."

Chapter Two:
Banned!

It was the first week back after the summer holidays. All of the Year 7s – the new kids – were lining up in the playground for their very first games lesson. All the boys lined up on one side for football, all the girls lined up on the other side for netball. All the girls, that is, except one. She was standing with the boys.

"What's your name?" asked the PE teacher.

"Hope Powell," said the girl.

"You should be lining up with the girls over the other side, Hope," said the PE teacher.

"But that line's for netball," said Hope. "I don't play netball. I play football."

The PE teacher sighed. He looked along the line of boys. "Any of you lads want a girl in your team?" he asked, with a laugh.

"She can be on our side," shouted one boy.

"No, ours!" yelled another. "She's the best player around here."

"That's right," agreed the first boy, "she's football crazy. She's always kicking a ball or a can about."

The PE teacher shrugged. "You seem to be popular, Hope," he said, with a smile. "OK. Join the boys and we'll see how you get on."

It didn't take long for Hope to show her skills. She became one of the stars of the school team. Everyone likes to watch an exciting player and soon parents and schoolmates were turning up to the school matches.

"At this rate, we could go on and win the schools' cup!" exclaimed the PE teacher excitedly.

But not everybody was happy.

During one match, Hope dribbled and dummied through the midfield to score a sensational goal. As the crowd cheered, one female spectator remained grim-faced.

After the match, the woman made her way across to the PE teacher.

Hope saw her talking to her teacher and jogged over to them.

"This lady is an official from the Women's Football Association," said the PE teacher.

"Really?" said Hope excitedly. She had no idea that there was an organisation devoted to women's football.

"As you saw, Hope's our star player!" said the PE teacher.

Hope beamed with pride. It was amazing! She'd been watched by an official from the Women's Football Association and she hadn't even known it!

"She may be your star player," replied the official. "But she's not playing in your team again!"

Hope couldn't believe what she was hearing. Her stomach turned. She began to feel ever-so-slightly sick. She gave her PE teacher a worried look.

"Apparently, girls are not allowed to play football with boys," he sighed.

"But I'm as good as the boys – better than most of them," said Hope. She realised her voice was very quiet and seemed to come from a long way away.

"I know," said the PE teacher.

"That has nothing to do with it," interrupted the official from the Women's Football Association. "Rules are rules. And you're banned from playing for the school team. Immediately!"

The official marched off. The PE teacher threw his hands up in the air in despair. "This is terrible," he groaned. "We'll never win the schools' cup now!"

Hope trudged away, fighting to hold back the tears. You may have lost a cup, she thought. But I've lost the chance to do the thing I love doing most of all.

Chapter Three:
The Lionesses

Hope mooched home from school, dribbling an empty drinks can along the pavement. She was still fed up about being banned from the school team. Why was she the only girl in the whole world who liked playing football?

"Hey!" Hope heard a voice calling behind her.

She turned round and found herself facing a girl from her school. The girl was older than she was, Year 9 probably, Hope guessed.

"I saw you playing in the match today," the girl said. "That was a fantastic goal!"

"Thanks," replied Hope. "It'll be my last for the school team, though. I've been banned from playing with the boys."

"I know," said the girl. "The news is all round the school. Everyone is furious. With you in the team we could have won the cup! Fat chance now, though. You're one of the best girl footballers I've seen."

Hope looked up at the girl in amazement. "One of the best girl footballers you've seen? You mean there are other girls who play football?" she asked. "I thought I was the only one."

"Don't be stupid! Of course you're not the only one! There's a whole lot of us that play down at The Den – you know, Millwall Football Club? We call ourselves The Lionesses."

"Wow! What do you have to do to join?"
asked Hope excitedly.

"Just turn up," the girl replied. She walked off,
down a side street.

"When?" Hope called after her.

"Sunday morning. Ten o'clock," the girl
called back.

The following Sunday, Hope made her way to Millwall Football Club. There were a whole lot of girls training on the pitch. Hope was one of the youngest, but she soon settled in. She always felt at home when she was playing football. After the match, the coach called her over.

"How would you like to play for the Millwall Lionesses?" the coach asked her. "We could do with a really talented, creative midfield player."

Hope was so excited, she could hardly open her mouth. But she did manage to smile and nod her head.

"You've gone very quiet," the coach said with a laugh.

"It's just that I didn't realise girls and women could play football... I mean properly," said Hope.

"Girls and women have been playing football as long as the men have," said the coach.

"Really?" Hope said. "I didn't know that."

The coach smiled. "Then I guess it's about time you learned all about Dick Kerr's Ladies."

Chapter Four:
Dick Kerr Ladies

The coach and Hope sat on the touchline.

"It all started during the First World War," explained the coach. "With lots of men away at war, women went to work in factories. One of these factories, called Dick, Kerr & Company, was in Preston, Lancashire."

"The women there were keen footballers. They got a team together to raise money to help wounded soldiers. They called themselves Dick Kerr Ladies."

"So, what happened after the war?" Hope asked.

"Dick Kerr Ladies became the England Women's Football Team. They played a series of four matches against France. They played at the grounds of Preston North End and Stockport, where they won; at Old Trafford where they drew; and at Stamford Bridge – where they lost 2–1. They played fast, exciting football. They also played one of the first floodlit football matches ever staged. Two anti-aircraft searchlights were used."

"Their biggest game was at Goodison Park; Everton's ground. In 1920, on Boxing Day, 53,000 spectators watched them play St Helen's, the second-best women's football team in England."

"Wow! That's a big crowd," said Hope.

"Too right – they were becoming more popular than the men's teams! Their star players, Lily Parr and Florrie Radford, became famous celebrities."

"But the Football Association were really worried. They believed that a woman's place was in the kitchen and not on the football pitch. They were determined to put a stop to women's football. And they did. On the 5th of December 1921, less than a year after Dick Kerr Ladies had thrilled a sell-out crowd at Goodison Park, women were banned from playing football at all Football Association grounds, a ban that lasted for 48 years."

"Just like I've been banned from playing in the school team," said Hope gloomily.

The coach nodded. "But women's football is becoming big again." He paused. "Now, I don't want you to get carried away, but I really think that you could be an England player in the making."

It was a lot for Hope to take in. She'd had no idea that there was an England Women's Football Team, let alone that she might be good enough one day to play in it.

"Mind you, you'll have to practice and train hard," said the coach.

"I don't mind doing that," replied Hope. She'd already made up her mind. She was going to play for England.

"Then I guess we'll be seeing you down here next Sunday?"

"You bet," said Hope.

She ran all the way home – and she didn't kick any cans. She didn't need to; she was a proper footballer now, a player for the Millwall Lionesses.

And, if she trained hard, a future England international! She couldn't wait to tell her mum the news.

Chapter Five:
Banned Again!

"Do you hear me, Hope? You are not going to that place again!"

Hope couldn't believe it. "Look, Mum, there's nothing wrong with The Den. It's a properly run football club. A professional club."

"Do you think I was born yesterday?" her mother retorted crossly. "I've read the paper. I know what it's like down there. It's full of hooligans!"

"But they've offered me a place in their women's team. And the coach said that if I work and train hard I could make the England international squad!"

"Girls don't play football," Hope's mum snapped. "At least, not properly brought up girls. It's no use arguing. You know my decision. You are not going to that football club again!"

Hope stormed up to her bedroom and slammed the door. Life just wasn't fair! First she had been banned from the school football team, now Mum had banned her from the Millwall Lionesses. Playing football was her ambition, playing football for England was her dream. Why would nobody let her do it? What was so wrong with it? It was no different to the Football Association banning women's football all those years ago.

But, Hope suddenly realised, it *was* different. There was a football club that wanted her and there was an England women's team. It wasn't any good just sitting on her bed feeling sorry for herself, though. She had to do something if she was going to realise her dream of one day playing for England.

The following Sunday morning Hope sneaked out the back door and made her way to The Den. She hated disobeying her mum, but she knew she'd hate missing the chance of playing for Millwall and for England even more.

She trained and played football all morning, then raced home and let herself into the house, minutes before her mum got back from church.

She did the same thing the following week, and the week after that.

But deep down she knew that one day, sooner or later, her mum would find out just what was going on…

And if that happened, it could all too easily be the end of her dream.

Chapter Six:
Number 1 Fan

"I've got some exciting news," the Lionesses's coach said. "I've managed to arrange a very special fixture. Our first evening match, under the floodlights."

A ripple of excitement ran around the changing room. But Hope's heart sank.

An evening match meant getting back late, so she couldn't hide this one from her mum. If she wanted to play, she would have to tell her mum the truth.

The thought filled Hope with dread. But she had to do it, to keep her dream alive. When she got home, she made her mum a cup of tea and then sat down opposite her in the kitchen.

"I know I shouldn't have, but I've been going down The Den," she confessed.

"I know," replied her mum.

"You know? But how?" asked Hope in disbelief.

Hope's mum just shrugged. "A mother knows these things," she said.

"I'm sorry I disobeyed you," said Hope. "It's just that football is so important to me."

"Well, I'm glad you've apologised," said Hope's mum. "And I suppose playing down at Millwall is safer than hanging about the streets with your brothers."

Then Hope told her mum about the evening match.

Hope's mum looked thoughtful. "OK. But I'll come along to see you play. Just this once, mind you," she said. "To make sure you get home all right. I can't pretend I'm looking forward to watching girls play football though."

Hope played like a dream in her first floodlit match. Her touch was sure, her passing sweet.

After the match, she asked her mum, "Have you changed your mind about girls' football?"

Her mum shook her head. "No." Hope noticed there was a twinkle in her eye. "Not yet. But give it a few years of you playing like that, and well…who knows…?"

Over the next few years, Hope carried on playing with the Millwall Lionesses. She trained hard and even when she wasn't down at The Den, she could be found kicking a football about somewhere.

Opposition coaches began to notice the Lionesses' young star and the England Women's football team coach regularly received reports about Hope's progress.

One day in 1983, the captain and coach of the England Women's football team sat down together to choose a squad for the European Championship match against the Republic of Ireland. Hope's name came up.

"But she's so young," frowned the coach.

"And she's so good," replied the captain.

Hope was just 16, the youngest player ever to have played in an England football international. The match was against the Republic of Ireland and England won 6–0.

The crowd cheered loud and long. One person though, cheered louder and longer than anyone else. She was sitting halfway up the main stand. It was Mrs Powell – Hope Powell's mum – and her Number 1 fan.

Fact file
Hope Powell

 Full name: Hope Powell OBE

 Born: London, 8th December 1966

1978	Selected for Millwall Lionesses' Women's team
1983	Makes her International debut for England against the Republic of Ireland
1984	Plays for England in the European Championship final
1989	Plays for Fulham in the women's FA Cup Final. Scores twice in a 3–2 defeat to Leasowe Pacific (Everton)
1991	Plays for Millwall Lionesses in the women's FA Cup Final. They beat Doncaster Belles 1–0
1996	Captain of the Croydon team that achieves the women's League and FA Cup double
1998	Retires as a player, having received 66 full England caps and scored 35 international goals

Appointed the first ever full-time National Coach of the England Women's Football team; the youngest ever England coach, the first female and the first black manager of an English national team

2002	Awarded an OBE in the Queen's birthday honours list
2003	Becomes the first woman to achieve the UEFA Pro-Licence coaching qualification
2007	The England Women's team reach the quarter finals of the World Cup, losing 3–0 to the USA

Monty Panesar

The five boys sitting on the boundary should all have been at school. Instead, they had come to watch a cricket match. Sachin Tendulkar, the greatest batsman in the world, was playing for the touring Indian side against the local county, Northamptonshire. The boys cheered his every stroke.

After the match, the tallest of the boys opened his kit bag and took out his cricket bat. "I'm going to get Sachin Tendulkar to sign this," he announced. He had a dream of becoming a great batsman like Tendulkar. "Well, I don't suppose any of us will ever see him again."

He wasn't to know it; but he was wrong, very wrong indeed.

Continue reading this story in
DREAM TO WIN: Monty Panesar

DREAM
TO WIN

Monty
Panesar

Roy Apps

Also by Roy Apps,
published by Franklin Watts:

978 0 7496 7057 3

978 0 7496 7056 6

978 0 7496 7054 2

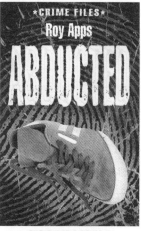

978 0 7496 7053 5